to Kevin Clark   from Rosemarie Lehmkuhl   9-10-80

The Book of Days

Cover illustration:
EMPEROR HUI-TSUNG, Chinese
The Five-Colored Parakeet (detail)
Sung period; early twelfth century
handscroll, ink and colors on silk
Maria Antoinette Evans Fund

The Book of Days

Museum of Fine Arts, Boston

Rutledge Books/Galison
New York, New York

The Boston Museum of Fine Arts is pleased to introduce *The Book of Days*, a special volume that combines the convenience of a desk diary with the lasting beauty of art reproductions from the Museum's collection.

The Book of Days is intended as a diary-date book in which to record special events, important personal dates, recollections, unuttered thoughts. It is unique in that it is not tied to any specific year. No matter when you start using it, there are always twelve months before you.

The works of art reproduced in *The Book of Days* are all from the Museum's collection. They span the centuries and include examples of Oriental, European, and American art.

It is sincerely hoped that *The Book of Days* will be of continuing use and delight and serve as a reminder of pleasant hours spent in the Museum.

Museum of Fine Arts, Boston

In the middle of the nineteenth century, Boston was the intellectual center of the yet to be completed United States. Boston published the books, set the intellectual tone, and combined thriving commerce with a leisurely but committed pursuit of spiritual and cultural values. What certainly must have irked the favored Bostonian as he returned from his travels to the European capitals was the lack in Boston of a properly constituted museum, or even a regularly organized symphony orchestra. Both those shortcomings were to be overcome as the century entered its final quarter.

On February 4, 1870, the Massachusetts Legislature granted a charter to a board of trustees, and the city provided a plot of land in the newly filled Back Bay, facing on what later became Copley Square. The nucleus of the new Museum was provided by the owners of several collections of art who desired to make them generally available to the public in a central place. Harvard wished to show its engravings; the Massachusetts Institute of Technology, its architectural casts; the Boston Athenaeum, its paintings, sculpture, and other objects; and the City of Boston, its most famous historic portraits.

Thus encouraged, the Museum began immediately a life of its own; while it started that very year to collect, to organize exhibitions, raise money, and execute all the things expected of the almost indefinable institution called a museum, it was not until July 4, 1876, that the infant Museum opened the doors of its first building on Copley Square. Thus it matched its own celebrations with the centennial of the nation's birth—a moment in time marked also by news dispatches on "Custer's Last Stand" in the West.

In those brave and far-off days, there was no income tax. Men of position could think big and act big. The Museum trustees did. Twenty-two years after they opened the doors, the need for a new building was apparent. They purchased twelve acres in the Back Bay Fens, and set off in committee to study all the museums in Europe, a project that occupied them for three months and produced a 200-page report on the ideal museum. The perspective rendering of the new Museum shows the building covering the entire twelve-acre site. Here was a building a little short of the Louvre in size, to be financed entirely by private resources.

The style followed the prevailing Classical mode, and so it was through a Greek portal that the first visitors entered the new Museum in November 1909. Sweeping vistas, ceremonial stairways, dramatic domes, and more columns awaited them within. Such expansive architecture today is unthinkable, but one cannot deny the grateful reflection that such grandiose American expressions stand a better chance of being preserved in the country's museums than in its railroad stations.

Six months were required to move the collections to the new building; among them were some of the greatest treasures in the Museum today. Even by that early date the primacy of the Museum in certain fields had already been established. Most conspicuous were surely the Oriental collections, already beyond compare in the world. Here the intellectualism of Boston was brought to bear on the Museum. Edward S. Morse, a self-taught Maine zoologist working in Salem, Massachusetts, ventured out to Japan in 1877, one year after the Museum opened its doors, in search of brachiopods. He stayed to find, appreciate, and collect the historic art of Japan in concert with his fellow townsman, Ernest Fenollosa, and another Boston friend, Dr. William Sturgis Bigelow. Together they literally uncovered a new world, one unknown to the West and half forgotten and even scorned by the Japanese themselves. Suffice it to say here, as an example of their contribution to the Museum, that their insight and devotion secured almost four-fifths of the five thousand Japanese and Chinese paintings now in the Boston collection.

This redoubtable trio set a pattern and tradition for the new Museum that obtain to this day. The Museum is not a legacy of ultra-rich patrons. Boston never boasted any Philadelphia Wideners, New York Morgans, or Pittsburgh Mellons. The Museum is rather a legacy of dedicated collectors, working in tandem with wise curators, who built their Museum — Boston's Museum — by their discernment, their desire for physical and intellectual adventure, and their need to follow their own paths and to become Lewis and Clarks in search of new frontiers.

January

1

2

3

4

5

6

7

8

9

10

YEN LI-PÊN (?), Chinese (died 673)
The Thirteen Emperors (detail)
T'ang period; seventh century
handscroll, ink and colors on silk
Denman Waldo Ross Collection

January

11

12

13

14

15

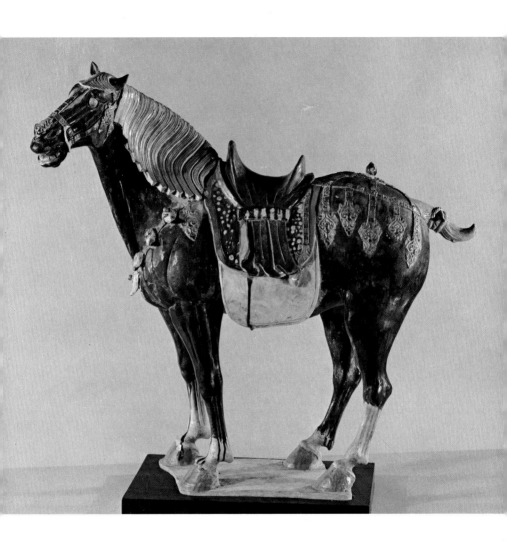

January

16

17

18

19

20

EMPEROR HUI-TSUNG, Chinese
The Five-Colored Parakeet (detail)
Sung period; early twelfth century
handscroll, ink and colors on silk
Maria Antoinette Evans Fund

January

21

22

23

24

25

Kuan-yin
Chinese, Sung period; circa twelfth century
polychromed wood
Harvey Edward Wetzel Fund

26

27

28

29

30

January-February

31

1

2

3

4

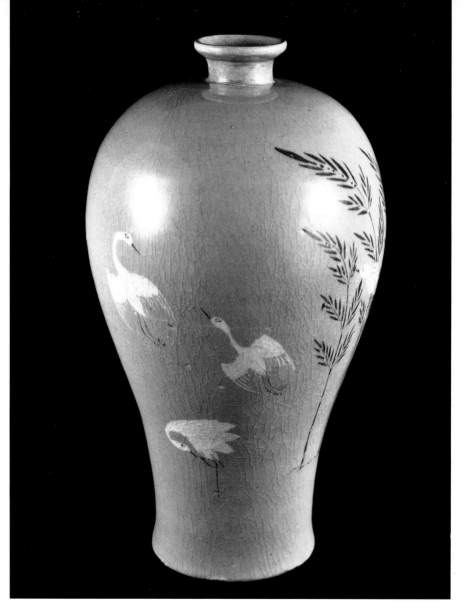

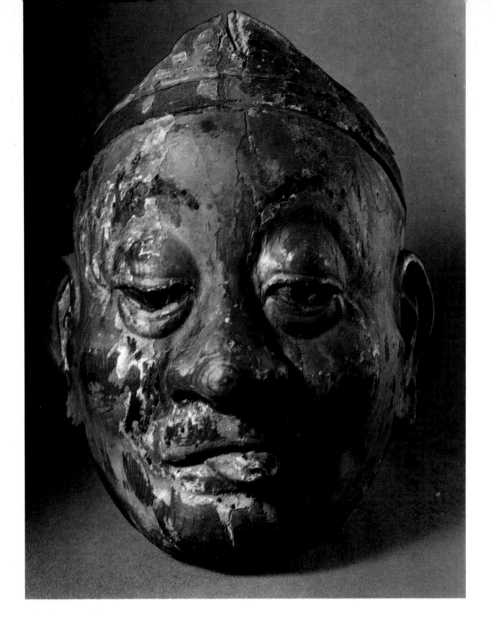

5

6

7

8

9

Gigaku Mask
Japanese, Heian period; circa eleventh century
polychromed wood
William Sturgis Bigelow Collection

February

10

11

12

13

14

KAIKEI, Japanese
Miroku Bosatsu
Kamakura period; 1189
wood, partially covered with gold lacquer
Chinese and Japanese Special Fund

February

15

16

17

18

19

Kibi Daijin Nittō E-kotoba (Kibi's Adventures in China) (detail)
Japanese, Heian period, late twelfth century
handscroll, ink and colors on paper
William Sturgis Bigelow Collection (by exchange)

February

20

21

22

23

24

Heiji Monogatari Emaki (The Burning of the Sanjo Palace) (detail)
Japanese, Kamakura period; late thirteenth century
handscroll, ink and colors on paper
Fenollosa-Weld Collection

25

26

27

28

29

1

Jar
Japanese, Edo period; late seventeenth century
Kakiëmon porcelain
Edward S. Morse Memorial Fund

March

2

3

4

5

6

March

7

8

9

10

11

Theater Scenes at Fukiya-chō (detail)
Chinese, Edo period; late seventeenth– early eighteenth century
six-fold screen; ink, colors, and gold on paper
Fenollosa-Weld Collection

March

12

13

14

15

16

OGATA KŌRIN, Japanese (1658– 1716)
Matsushima (detail)
Edo period; early eighteenth century
six-fold screen; ink and colors on paper
Fenollosa-Weld Collection

March

17

18

19

20

21

TORII KIYONAGA, Japanese (1752–1815)
A Mother and Daughter Under a Willow Tree
Edo period; late eighteenth century
ink and colors on silk
William Sturgis Bigelow Collection

March

22

23

24

25

26

March

27

28

29

30

31

The Bodhisattva's Bath in the Niranjana River (detail)
Indian (Amaravati), first century
greenish limestone
Ross Collection

April

1

2

3

4

5

6

7

8

9

10

Hawk Attacking a Duck
Persian (Iran), tenth–eleventh century
stucco
University Museum–Museum of Fine Arts
Persian Expedition

April

11

12

13

14

15

أنا فصب فيه خلا حامضا ثم علق الرصاص فيه و
طن فما أنا وقره أبا ما ثم أفيه فان كان

فاجردده ثم راعك حتى لا يبقى منه شئ واذا أر
دته فاعجنه خلا حامضا ثم نسه في الشمس الح

April

16

17

18

19

20

April

21

22

23

24

25

King Mycerinus and His Queen (detail)
Egyptian, Dynasty IV; circa 2600– 2500 B.C.
schist
Harvard-Boston Expedition

April

26

27

28

29

30

Deir el Bersheh Coffin (detail)
Egyptian, Dynasty XII; circa 1870 B.C.
painting on wood
Harvard-Boston Expedition

May

1

2

3

4

5

Model Procession of Offering Bearers
Egyptian, Dynasty XII; circa 1870 B.C.
painted wood
Harvard-Boston Expedition

6

7

8

9

10

Relief of King Ay
Egyptian, Dynasty XVIII; circa 1342 B.C.
alabaster
Gift of Edward Waldo Forbes

May

11

12

13

14

15

16

17

18

19

20

Snake Goddess (detail)
Minoan, circa 1500 B.C.
ivory and gold
Gift of Mrs. W. Scott Fitz

May

21

22

23

24

25

A Divine Contest and Attendants (detail)
Greek, circa 470– 460 B.C.
marble, three-sided relief
Pierce Foundation

26

27

28

29

30

Earring with Winged Charioteer
Greek, fourth century B.C.
gold
Pierce Foundation

May-June

31

1

2

3

4

5

6

7

8

9

Arsinoë II of Egypt
Greek, circa 300 B.C.
bronze
Perkins Collection

June

10

11

12

13

14

Oliphant
Italian, Salerno (?), circa 1100
ivory
Maria Antoinette Evans Fund

15

16

17

18

19

ARNOLFO DI CAMBIO, Italian (circa 1245–1310)
Deacon and Acolytes
1264–1267
marble
Grace M. Edwards Fund

June

20

21

22

23

24

Christ in Majesty with Scenes of the Old and New Testaments
Spanish, Catalonian, twelfth century
detached fresco, from the church of Santa Maria de Mur
Maria Antoinette Evans Fund

June

25

26

27

28

29

June-July

30

1

2

3

4

5

6

7

8

9

Virgin and Child (detail)
French (Ile-de-France), circa 1200
polychromed and gilt oak
William Francis Warden Fund

July

10

11

12

13

14

GIOVANNI DI PAOLO, Italian (1403–1482)
The Virgin of Humility
tempera on panel
Maria Antoinette Evans Fund

15

16

17

18

19

Master of the Barberini Panels (GIOVANNI ANGELO D'ANTONIO DA CAMERINO?), Italian
Presentation of the Virgin in the Temple
fifteenth century
tempera on panel, from the Ducal Palace of Urbino
Charles Potter Kling Fund

July

20

21

22

23

24

25

26

27

28

29

ROGIER VAN DER WEYDEN, Flemish (circa 1399–1464)
St. Luke Painting the Virgin (detail)
oil on oak panel
Gift of Mr. and Mrs. Henry Lee Higginson

July-August

30

31

1

2

3

Wild Men and Moors (detail)
German, late fourteenth century
tapestry weaving, wool and linen yarns
Charles Potter Kling Fund

4

5

6

7

8

Christ Before Pilate (detail)
Franco-Flemish, late fifteenth century
wool and silk tapestry, from a series depicting the history of the Passion of Christ
Gift of Robert Treat Paine II in memory of his son, Walter Cabot Paine

August

9

10

11

12

13

August

14

15

16

17

18

PETER PAUL RUBENS, Flemish (1577–1640)
The Head of Cyrus Brought to Queen Tomyris (detail)
oil on canvas
Robert J. Edwards Fund

August

19

20

21

22

23

August

24

25

26

27

28

DIEGO VELÁZQUEZ DE SILVA, Spanish (1599–1660)
Don Baltasar Carlos and His Dwarf (detail)
1631
oil on canvas
Henry Lillie Pierce Fund

August-September

29

30

31

1

2

September

3

4

5

6

7

JACOB VAN RUISDAEL, Dutch (1628–1682)
A Rough Sea
circa 1670
oil on canvas
William Francis Warden Fund

September

8

9

10

11

12

September

13

14
1980 –
Kevin's 1st day home – Cincy family here – no problems.

15

16

17

NICOLAS POUSSIN, French (1594–1665)
Mars and Venus
circa 1630
oil on canvas
Augustus Hemenway and Arthur Wheelwright Funds

September

18

19

20

21

22

ANTOINE WATTEAU, French (1684–1721)
La Perspective
circa 1716
oil on canvas
Maria Antoinette Evans Fund

23

24

25

26

27

September-October

28

29

30

1

2

GIOVANNI BATTISTA TIEPOLO, Italian (1696–1770)
Time Unveiling Truth (detail)
oil on canvas
Charles Potter Kling Fund

October

3

4

5

6

7

CANALETTO (GIOVANNI ANTONIO CANALE), Italian (1697–1768)
Bacino di San Marco
circa 1745
oil on canvas
Abbott Lawrence, Seth K. Sweetser, and Charles Edward French Funds

October

8

9

10

11

12

13

14

15 1980 - K's cord finally fell off! He's very alert, knows me + Jim, I think B, too!

16

17

October

18

19

20

21

22

23

24

25

26

27

JOHN SINGLETON COPLEY, American (1738–1815)
Paul Revere
circa 1768–1770
oil on canvas
Gift of William B. Joseph and Edward H. R. Revere

October-November

28

29

30

31

1

November

2

3

4

5

6

November

7

8

9

10

11

November

12

13

14

15

16

EDOUARD MANET, French (1832–1883)
The Street Singer
1862
oil on canvas
Bequest of Sarah Choate Sears in memory of her husband, Joshua Montgomery Sears

November

17 *K turned from tummy to back for first time.*

18

19

20

21

November

22

23

24

25

26

CLAUDE MONET, French (1840–1926)
Fisherman's Cottage on the Cliffs at Varengeville
1882
oil on canvas
Bequest of Anna Perkins Rogers

November-December

27

28

29

30

1

PIERRE AUGUSTE RENOIR, French (1841–1919)
Le Bal à Bougival
1883
oil on canvas
Anna Mitchell Richards Fund

December

2

3

4

5

6

PAUL CÉZANNE, French (1839–1906)
The Turn in the Road
circa 1880
oil on canvas
Bequest of John T. Spaulding

December

7

8

9

10

11

12

13

14

15

16

PAUL GAUGUIN, French (1848–1903)
D'où venons-nous? Que sommes-nous? Où allons-nous? (detail)
oil on burlap
Purchase, Arthur Gordon Tompkins Residuary Fund

December

17

18

19

20

21

22

23

24

25

26

PABLO PICASSO, Spanish (1881–1973)
Standing Figure
1908
oil on canvas
Juliana Cheney Edwards Collection

December

27

28

29

30

31

CONSTANTIN BRANCUSI, Rumanian (1876–1957)
The Golden Fish
1924
polished brass and steel
William Francis Warden Fund

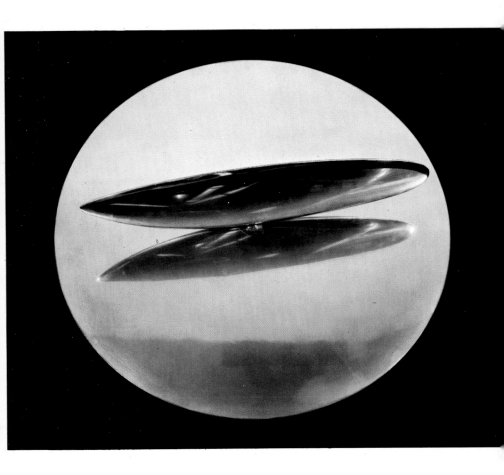

Index

Notes

Notes

Notes

Notes